Once "a pun" a Time
a Time

HA HA

A guide to reading and telling jokes for kids

Wolf Cub Chlo

FREE gift for readers

Email us at:

Jenn@wolfcubchlo.com

to get your free bonuses!

- 31 Days of Fun Reading Challenge
- Fun Reading Bingo printable game card: Plan your reading activities around the seasons for additional fun with done-for-you seasonal reading activities.
- Coloring pages for quick on-the-go activities and a few other surprises.

Just title the email ""FREE Gift for readers" for your surprises!

Once "a pun" a Time
A guide to reading and telling jokes for kids
Joke book for kids

Dedication

I dedicate my first joke book to my mommy, daddy,
nana and everyone else I love most. You keep me
smiling every day and I hope I make you smile too.
So let's keep smiling together!

Who is Wolf Cub Chlo?

> Hi and howwwwl are you? My name is Chloé, but I call myself Wolf Cub because, although I love all other animals, I especially love wolves. I love my family and we all love to laugh. But 2020 was such a sad year that I wanted to find a way to use my brain to make more people smile.

Part I: WANNA HEAR SOMETHING "PUNNY?"

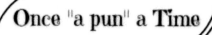

Once "a pun" a Time

What did the snowflake say to the penguin?

You know me snow well.

Once "a pun" a Time
What did the person say to the hurt cat?
Me-OUCH, that's gotta hurt!

Once "a pun" a Time

How did the blueberry feel during the rain?

Berry blue!

Why did the nodding dolphin get in trouble?

For being too "noddy" (naughty.)

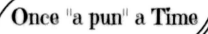
Once "a pun" a Time

Where do small children grow their letters?

In Kinder-GARDEN!

Once "a pun" a Time

Why couldn't the librarians hangout over the weekend?

Because they were booked and busy.

Once "a pun" a Time

What kind of attendance did the cat get in school?

Puurrrrrr-fect!

Part II: HOW TO WRITE YOUR OWN JOKES?

Hey, want to know a secret to writing your own jokes? It's just being silly with words! Let me show you the trick! Homophones are words that sound exactly the same but mean something totally different. Like the word "ball" and "bawl." See! They sound exactly the same but use different letters. A pun is just a joke that uses a homophone in it!. I loooooove puns! Let's give you a chance to try to create your own puns.

Another way I try to create jokes is by telling a silly story around any word. Like the horse joke in Part I. Horses "gitty up" when they run, so I just created a funny story around a horse that fell and couldn't run anymore.

Now, it's YOUR turn to create silly jokes! To help, I will give you a word and picture so you can write something silly about it. Ready? Here we go!

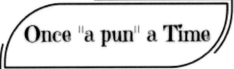

Once "a pun" a Time

Orange ya' glad you get to write your own jokes too? Use the word orange to create a silly story or sentence.

_____

_____

_____

_____

_____

_____

Now, try the words knight and night. See if you can create another silly pun with these words. Use the pictures to help if you need it.

_____

_____

_____

_____

_____

_____

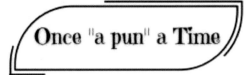

Once "a pun" a Time

Here are the words: eye and I. EYE need new glasses, no seriously I do...Well, not, really since I don't even wear glasses, but you get my drift.

Did you know you can tell how big a diamond is by measuring the carats? But do bunnies eat big carats or eat big carrots? Now you try!

_____

_____

_____

_____

_____

_____

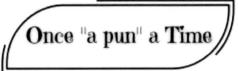

Once "a pun" a Time

When you won, were you number one? Power your energy to create another silly story or joke.

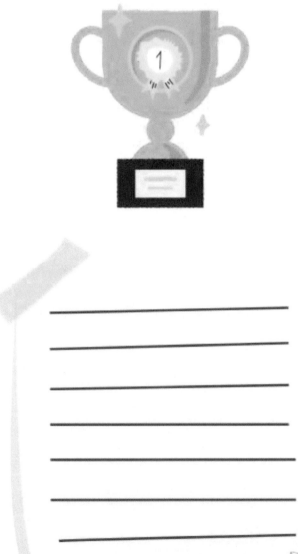

_____

_____

_____

_____

_____

_____

Once "a pun" a Time

CONGRATULATIONS WOLF PACK!!!!!!

You just wrote your first jokes! Don't stop here; keep going!

There are hundreds of homophones. Try using as many as you can to create a silly joke, pun, riddle or even a tongue twister!! Try creating jokes with a partner! Write down random words together and then take turns using those same words to create a silly story or joke. I would love to hear them, but would you prefer my presence or presents? Let's keep the show going!

THANKS FOR HOWLING BY

Thanks for reading my jokes and I hope they made you smile. If they did, then my job is done! If you were able to make someone else smile, then my job is done! I would also love to hear the jokes you made too so I can keep smiling. Send all work to support@wolfcubchlo.fans for a chance to be featured.

Please let others know how you enjoyed the book by leaving a review here: https://amzn.to/3qxvQHR

Remember there's always something to smile about.
Until next time, buy... Oops, I mean bye.
Sincere Howls,
Wolf Cub Chlo

Other books:
Once 'a pun' a Time ART-ivity book for kids –
https://amzn.to/3nxZbQx

Are you looking for more fun activities to do with your
children? Check out our "Bundle of Jokes" deal:
https://wolfcubchlo.com/products/bundle-of-jokes-deal

Have you been searching for answers on how to reduce
your child's screen time? Looking for a productive and
healthy way to solve this problem while keeping the
lines of communication open with your child? Check out
our "Screen Time Tips Parenting Bundle:"
https://wolfcubchlo.com/products/screen-time-tips-
parenting-bundle

Social Media:
Instagram: https://www.instagram.com/wolfcubchlo_fans/

Made in the USA
Coppell, TX
02 February 2022

72856556R00019